TEST YOUR PAIRS PLAY

Those who wish to succeed at match-pointed pairs have to modify their approach to the game to take account of the method of scoring that is used. The winners of major tournaments invariably come from a select group of players who have learned to adjust their tactics to the vagaries of the pairs game.

The main difference is that making or defeating the contract is not all-important. The aim is to score more or lose fewer points than the other pairs handling your cards. Overtricks and undertricks take on an importance that they do not have in other forms of the game, and it is vital to recognise this factor in planning your line of play or defence.

If you have difficulty in coming to terms with the techniques of pairs play, you are sure to benefit from a study of this quiz book. Author Hugh Kelsey, a grand master of bridge and an author of world renown, explains the eccentric logic of the pairs game and shows how to overcome the hurdles.

D1638031

TEST YOUR PAIRS PLAY

by

HUGH KELSEY

LONDON
VICTOR GOLLANCZ LTD
in association with Peter Crawley
1985

First published in Great Britain 1985
by Victor Gollancz Ltd,
14 Henrietta Street, London WC2E 8QJ

British Library Cataloguing in Publication Data
Kelsey, H.W.
   Test your pairs play.—(Master
   bridge series)
   1. Contract bridge
   I. Title   II. Series
   795.41′5   GV1282.3

   ISBN 0–575–03673–7

Photoset and printed in Great Britain
by Photobooks (Bristol) Ltd

TEST YOUR PAIRS PLAY

INTRODUCTION

Players taking part in their first match-pointed pairs event are invariably disappointed with their results. It takes time to adjust to the effects of the method of scoring used. The making or defeating of the contract is no longer all-important, as it is at team or rubber bridge. The aim is simply to score more or lose fewer points than the other pairs handling your cards. The aggregate margin by which you outscore the others is of no importance. All that matters is the number of pairs that you beat. You receive two match points for each pair you beat and one for each pair you tie with.

A shift in strategy and tactics is needed if you are to score well at pairs. For each board you must determine a trick target which you consider will give you a reasonable score. This target may or may not coincide with the making or the defeating of the contract. For example, it is no good making nine tricks at no trumps for a score of 600 if all the other pairs are scoring 620 in four hearts. You need an overtrick and a score of 630 to beat those pairs, and you may have to put your contract at risk in trying for the overtrick. If you go down you will score zero, but plus 600 would have been close to zero anyway.

Every board is of equal importance. The same number of match-points are at stake whether the contract is a humble part-score or a grand slam. Constant vigilance is therefore essential. It can cost just as much to let declarer make an overtrick in two clubs as it can to let the grand slam home.

The tendency in defence is towards safety. Avoid leads that may present declarer with a trick he could not otherwise have scored. In playing the hand the tendency is away from safety. In the absence of special circumstances, it is usually right for declarer to try for as many tricks as possible.

This book is designed to sharpen your play and defence in many situations of the sort that constantly arise in the pairs game. If you can acquire a working understanding of the eccentric logic of pairs, you will soon achieve higher placings in the tournaments you enter.

The problems are posed on odd-numbered pages with only two hands on view. A bidding sequence is provided, but this can be ignored except where it provides a clue to the opponents' holdings. The opening lead is given along with, in some cases, an account of the early play. You are then invited to continue the play or the defence. Try to work out the solution for yourself before reading on. If stuck, you may find some help in the next paragraph where the problem is summarised and the options set out.

There is not much variation in the level of difficulty of the problems, although towards the end they tend to become a little harder. But by that time you will have adjusted to the type of thinking that is required. You can consider yourself a competent pairs player if you come up with the right answer to more than twenty of these problems. More than twenty-five right means that you are surely winning your share of tournaments, while more than thirty marks you as a pairs expert. Good Luck!

PROBLEM 1

```
        ♠ 7 5
        ♡ A J 6 4
        ◇ K 10 6 2
        ♣ 8 7 2
```

```
        ♠ A 8 4
        ♡ K Q 7 5
        ◇ Q J 7
        ♣ J 10 4
```

Love all
Dealer South

The Bidding

SOUTH	WEST	NORTH	EAST
1 NT	Pass	Pass	Pass

The Lead

West leads the six of spades to his partner's queen. You hold off and East continues with the ten of spades, West dropping the two under your ace. How should you continue?

Review

Clearly you have missed the best contract, since two hearts appears to be lay-down. Now you have a typical match-point decision to make. Should you settle for five tricks and a score of minus 100, or should you try to steal a trick or two in diamonds before the defenders know too much about your hand?

Solution

There is no way you can beat those who play in two hearts, but will there be many of them? In estimating the prospects you have to consider not only the alternative contracts for your side but also those for the opponents. The weak no trump – a crude device in some ways – has prevented you from reaching your best contract of two hearts but it has pre-empted your opponents. Neither dared to contest at the two-level, but it seems that they have a 5–3 spade fit and West might well have come in with a bid of one spade if you had opened one heart or one club. And it is clear that you have no more than five tricks in defence against a spade contract.

If others are conceding 110 defending against two spades, you can well afford to lose 100 in one no trump. All the indications are that you should not be greedy. Make sure of your five tricks by cashing the hearts first and settle for two down.

The complete deal:

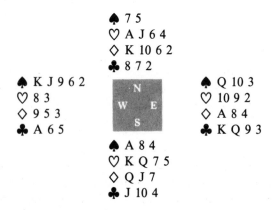

Anyone who tries to steal a diamond trick is likely to finish three down, and minus 150 is sure to be a poor score.

PROBLEM 2

$$\spadesuit\ A\ 6\ 3$$
$$\heartsuit\ K\ 9\ 4$$
$$\diamondsuit\ Q\ J\ 6$$
$$\clubsuit\ 9\ 8\ 6\ 2$$

$$\spadesuit\ K\ Q\ 5$$
$$\heartsuit\ A\ Q\ 10\ 6\ 2$$

N-S game

$$\diamondsuit\ K\ 7\ 4$$

Dealer South

$$\clubsuit\ J\ 7$$

The Bidding

SOUTH	WEST	NORTH	EAST
1 NT	2 ♠	3 NT	Pass
Pass	Pass		

The Lead

West leads the jack of spades to the three, eight and king. You try a small diamond to the queen, West playing the three and East the two. How should you continue?

Review

Now your contract is safe on the assumption that the hearts are worth five tricks. The only thing that remains to be considered is whether making nine tricks at no trumps will give you a satisfactory score.

Solution

On the last hand the weak no trump caused problems; now it's the turn of the strong no trump. Many players refuse to open one no trump when holding a good five-card major, and there is much to be said for this style. Anyone who opens one heart on this hand is likely to finish in a heart game, and you can see that ten tricks will be available in hearts as long as the breaks are not too bad. Your score of 600 will look pretty sick in comparison with all the 620's on the sheet.

You need an overtrick to beat those who play in the heart game and you should therefore play a second diamond at trick three. This courts defeat, but it is a risk that should be taken.

The complete deal:

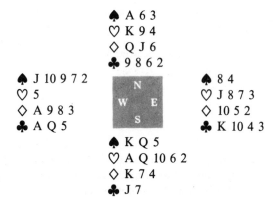

```
                    ♠ A 6 3
                    ♡ K 9 4
                    ◇ Q J 6
                    ♣ 9 8 6 2
  ♠ J 10 9 7 2         N            ♠ 8 4
  ♡ 5                             ♡ J 8 7 3
  ◇ A 9 8 3      W        E        ◇ 10 5 2
  ♣ A Q 5                          ♣ K 10 4 3
                      S
                    ♠ K Q 5
                    ♡ A Q 10 6 2
                    ◇ K 7 4
                    ♣ J 7
```

If West finds the club switch after winning the ace of diamonds you will go down, but the difference between plus 600 and minus 100 on the score-sheet will be negligible. If West continues spades, however, you will achieve a top score instead of a near-bottom.

PROBLEM 3

♠ A J 9 7 3
♡ K 7 6 2
◇ Q
♣ 6 5 4

♠ Q 10
♡ 9 5
◇ A J 7 4 2
♣ 9 8 7 3

N-S game
Dealer South

The Bidding

SOUTH	WEST	NORTH	EAST
1 NT*	Pass	2 ♣	Pass
2 ◇	Pass	3 ♠	Pass
3 NT	Pass	Pass	Pass

15–17

The Lead

You select the normal lead of the four of diamonds. Surprisingly, East produces the king and returns the eight of diamonds, which South covers with the ten. You win with the jack and a club is thrown from dummy. How should you continue?

Review

Partner's play indicates an original holding of three diamonds, so you know that South still has the nine guarded. If you could find partner with an entry, a further diamond return would put the contract two down. Is this worth trying or is it too ambitious?

Solution

There is just room for partner to have an ace, either in hearts or clubs, or he could have the king of spades. In any of these cases you may be able to defeat the contract if you find the right switch. But the odds must be against this. Partner's remaining high cards are more likely to be minor honours in clubs or hearts which will be of little use to the defence. Your spade holding is particularly depressing, for you can see that declarer will make five tricks in the suit if he has the doubleton king.

There is no certainty of being right in these situations but on balance it will pay to cash the ace of diamonds, thereby making sure of three tricks for the defence.

The complete deal:

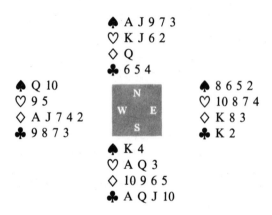

♠ A J 9 7 3
♡ K J 6 2
♢ Q
♣ 6 5 4

♠ Q 10
♡ 9 5
♢ A J 7 4 2
♣ 9 8 7 3

♠ 8 6 5 2
♡ 10 8 7 4
♢ K 8 3
♣ K 2

♠ K 4
♡ A Q 3
♢ 10 9 6 5
♣ A Q J 10

As you can see, any switch allows declarer to score eleven tricks.

PROBLEM 4

♠ K J 4
♡ A 10 3
◇ A 9 7 6 3
♣ J 2

♠ A Q 10 8 6 3
♡ 6
◇ K 5 4
♣ Q 10 5

Game all
Dealer South

The Bidding

SOUTH	WEST	NORTH	EAST
1♠	Pass	2◇	Pass
2♠	Pass	4♠	Pass
Pass	Pass		

The Lead

West leads the queen of hearts. How do you plan the play?

Review

This looks like the standard contract. If any gambler plays in three no trumps he will make no more than nine tricks on a heart lead. Ten tricks in spades will give you a fair score, and that is just a matter of winning the first trick, drawing trumps and establishing a trick in clubs. Might you do better?

Solution

At teams this hand would be routine, but at pairs you have to press a little harder. You can see that the defenders can always cash three tricks against your game, but this may not be clear to West. Make life difficult for him by playing low from dummy at trick one, allowing the queen of hearts to hold the trick.

The complete deal:

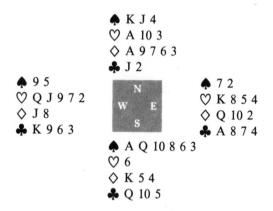

```
                    ♠ K J 4
                    ♡ A 10 3
                    ◇ A 9 7 6 3
                    ♣ J 2
 ♠ 9 5                              ♠ 7 2
 ♡ Q J 9 7 2        N              ♡ K 8 5 4
 ◇ J 8          W       E          ◇ Q 10 2
 ♣ K 9 6 3          S              ♣ A 8 7 4
                    ♠ A Q 10 8 6 3
                    ♡ 6
                    ◇ K 5 4
                    ♣ Q 10 5
```

It is hard for West to find the club switch that nets three tricks for the defence, and even if he does find it your contract is in no danger. The defenders may score one heart and two clubs, but after drawing trumps you can eventually discard your diamond loser on the heart ace.

The bonus comes when West fails to find the club switch. Now you can draw trumps, discard a diamond on the ace of hearts and ruff the third round of diamonds to establish the suit. A trump puts you back in dummy, and two losing clubs go away on the long diamonds. Deceptive technique thus earns you 650 and a top score.

PROBLEM 5

♠ 7 6 4
♡ 3
♢ Q J 5
♣ K Q J 6 5 2

♠ A K Q 5
♡ Q 9 8 2
♢ 8 6
♣ A 8 3

Love all
Dealer South

The Bidding

SOUTH	WEST	NORTH	EAST
1♠	2♡	2♠	Pass
Pass	Pass		

The Lead

West leads the ace of hearts on which East plays the ten, then switches to the ten of spades, East following with the two. How do you plan the play?

Review

Four spades and six clubs would give you ten tricks and an excellent score. For that matter, if you ruffed a heart in dummy you might even make eleven tricks. Is this a realistic trick target?

Solution

As always, you have to consider the other possible contracts your way. Partner's raise to two spades was a little unorthodox, and it is likely that others will play in clubs or even in no trumps. Eight tricks are likely to be the limit in no trumps, since it will not be too hard for West to find the diamond switch after cashing a top heart. Those who play in clubs will make ten tricks for a score of 130.

It follows that your target in spades need be no higher than nine tricks. And there is a good way of ensuring nine tricks even when the trumps are 4–2. Just hold off the first spade, allowing the ten to win. You can cope with any continuation, scoring at least three spades and six clubs for 140.

The complete deal:

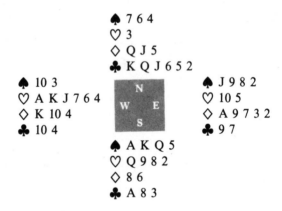

```
                    ♠ 7 6 4
                    ♡ 3
                    ◇ Q J 5
                    ♣ K Q J 6 5 2
 ♠ 10 3                              ♠ J 9 8 2
 ♡ A K J 7 6 4        N              ♡ 10 5
 ◇ K 10 4          W     E           ◇ A 9 7 3 2
 ♣ 10 4              S               ♣ 9 7
                    ♠ A K Q 5
                    ♡ Q 9 8 2
                    ◇ 8 6
                    ♣ A 8 3
```

The greedy ones who win the first trump and ruff a heart will end up with only eight tricks and a poor match-point result.

PROBLEM 6

♠ 7 6 2
♡ A 6 5 3
◇ A K Q 8 3
♣ 7

♠ A K 5
♡ K J
◇ 6 4
♣ Q 9 8 5 4 3

Love all
Dealer South

The Bidding

SOUTH	WEST	NORTH	EAST
1 NT	Pass	2♣	Pass
2◇	Pass	3 NT	Pass
Pass	Pass		

The Lead

West leads the two of hearts to the three, nine and jack. How do you plan the play?

Review

Your unorthodox opening bid of one no trump appears to have worked out well. After unblocking the king of hearts, you could play safe for four diamonds by ducking the first round of the suit. Should you employ this safety play?

Solution

It is rare to go for safety at pairs, but you must take account of the fact that you have received a favourable lead away from the queen of hearts. Three no trumps is likely to be the final contract at most tables, but at some North will bid hearts on the way to game. This will inhibit the heart lead, and those declarers who receive a spade lead will make nine tricks only if the diamonds break 3-3. A 4-2 break is more likely, in which case the declarers will concede the fourth diamond and make eight tricks – the same number that you will make if you play the diamonds from the top.

Since you are a trick ahead of the field at the moment you should consolidate your advantage by playing safe. Cash the king of hearts and duck a diamond. On balance this will bring in more points than playing for the 3-3 break.

The complete deal:

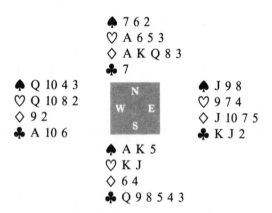

	♠ 7 6 2	
	♡ A 6 5 3	
	◇ A K Q 8 3	
	♣ 7	
♠ Q 10 4 3		♠ J 9 8
♡ Q 10 8 2		♡ 9 7 4
◇ 9 2		◇ J 10 7 5
♣ A 10 6		♣ K J 2
	♠ A K 5	
	♡ K J	
	◇ 6 4	
	♣ Q 9 8 5 4 3	

PROBLEM 7

♠ K 6 4 3
♡ 9 8 4 2
♢ A J 9
♣ 9 3

♠ A 8 5
♡ A K Q 10 6
♢ 10 2
♣ A 7 5

Game all
Dealer South

The Bidding

SOUTH	WEST	NORTH	EAST
1♡	Pass	2♡	Pass
4♡	Pass	Pass	Pass

The Lead

West leads the jack of spades to dummy's king and East drops the queen. You draw trumps in three rounds, West discarding a small club and a small diamond, and then run the ten of diamonds to East's queen. The two of spades is returned to your ace. How should you continue?

Review

You can play safe for ten tricks, losing one spade, one diamond and one club. The question is whether you should risk a further diamond finesse in an attempt to dispose of your losing spade. If the finesse succeeds you will make eleven tricks but if it fails you will be held to nine.

Solution

The finesse may look like a fifty-fifty chance, but in practice as well as in theory it is more than twice as likely to succeed as it is to fail. It is just a matter of percentages. The fact that East won the first diamond with the queen affords a presumption that he is unlikely to have the king as well.

You may find it easier to consider the probabilities *a priori*. From the start there was a 52% chance that the diamond honours would be divided and only a 24% chance that East would have them both. These figures remain constant, which means that there is a 68% chance that the second diamond finesse will succeed.

The chance of making an overtrick is high enough to justify putting the contract at risk. You should therefore finesse the jack of diamonds in an attempt to make eleven tricks.

The complete deal:

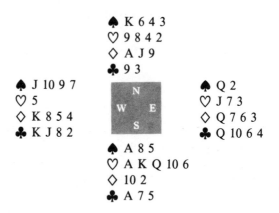

```
                    ♠ K 6 4 3
                    ♡ 9 8 4 2
                    ◇ A J 9
                    ♣ 9 3
  ♠ J 10 9 7                      ♠ Q 2
  ♡ 5              N              ♡ J 7 3
  ◇ K 8 5 4     W     E           ◇ Q 7 6 3
  ♣ K J 8 2        S              ♣ Q 10 6 4
                    ♠ A 8 5
                    ♡ A K Q 10 6
                    ◇ 10 2
                    ♣ A 7 5
```

PROBLEM 8

♠ A 9 3
♡ A 6 5
♢ A J 10 8 2
♣ Q 4

♠ 10 5
♡ K Q 8 3
♢ Q 9 4
♣ A K 10 2

Love all
Dealer South

The Bidding

SOUTH	WEST	NORTH	EAST
1 NT	Pass	3 NT	Pass
Pass	Pass		

The Lead

West leads the six of spades. How do you plan the play?

Review

At team or rubber bridge you would naturally hold up the ace of spades until the third round. Since you are taking the diamond finesse into the East hand, you would then be assured of ten tricks if the spades are 5–3. At pairs one alternative is to hold up just once in spades. This makes a small concession to safety in case the spades are 6–2 and still assures you of twelve tricks when the diamond finesse is right. Is there anything better?

Solution

The disadvantage of holding up in spades is that you may make fewer than the optimum number of tricks if the diamond finesse is working. When West has the king of diamonds, all thirteen tricks will be there for the taking if the hearts break 3–3 or if the jack of clubs comes down.

If you win the first spade, cross to hand with a heart and finesse in diamonds, you will go down when the finesse fails and the spades are 5–3 or 6–2. But you will be sure of making all the tricks that are available when the diamond finesse is right.

At pairs the odds are heavily against the hold-up. You should win the first trick with the ace of spades and go for broke.

The complete deal:

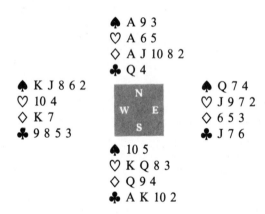

```
                    ♠ A 9 3
                    ♡ A 6 5
                    ◇ A J 10 8 2
                    ♣ Q 4
    ♠ K J 8 6 2                      ♠ Q 7 4
    ♡ 10 4          N                ♡ J 9 7 2
    ◇ K 7        W     E             ◇ 6 5 3
    ♣ 9 8 5 3       S                ♣ J 7 6
                    ♠ 10 5
                    ♡ K Q 8 3
                    ◇ Q 9 4
                    ♣ A K 10 2
```

PROBLEM 9

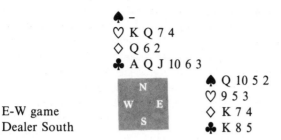

♠ –
♡ K Q 7 4
◇ Q 6 2
♣ A Q J 10 6 3

♠ Q 10 5 2
♡ 9 5 3
◇ K 7 4
♣ K 8 5

E-W game
Dealer South

The Bidding

SOUTH	WEST	NORTH	EAST
1 NT*	Pass	2 ♣	Pass
2 ♠	Pass	3 ♣	Pass
3 ◇	Pass	3 ♡	Pass
3 NT	Pass	Pass	Pass

12–14

The Lead

In spite of South's bid of two spades, West leads the six of spades against the no trump game. A heart is discarded from dummy and your spade queen holds the trick, South following with the three. How should you continue?

Review

You know from the bidding that South has four spades and West five, and you must hope that South's only significant card in the suit is the ace. Declarer might still make his contract by holding up the ace of spades three times before finessing in clubs. Can you deflect him from this course?

Solution

Declarers are always reluctant to give up the chance of overtricks by holding up too often. In this case South will be particularly keen to make ten tricks in no trumps in order to outscore anyone who plays in clubs. You should therefore try to persuade him to take the ace of spades on the third round by returning the ten of spades – not the normal two.

If South gains the impression that you started with three spades he will see no reason to hold up three times. He will take his ace on the third round and finesse in clubs, hoping to make at least ten tricks and possibly eleven.

South's chagrin when you win the king of clubs and produce a fourth spade to defeat the contract will be something to behold.

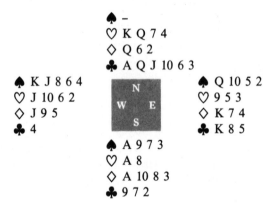

```
                    ♠ –
                    ♡ K Q 7 4
                    ◇ Q 6 2
                    ♣ A Q J 10 6 3
  ♠ K J 8 6 4                        ♠ Q 10 5 2
  ♡ J 10 6 2        N               ♡ 9 5 3
  ◇ J 9 5         W   E             ◇ K 7 4
  ♣ 4               S               ♣ K 8 5
                    ♠ A 9 7 3
                    ♡ A 8
                    ◇ A 10 8 3
                    ♣ 9 7 2
```

PROBLEM 10

♠ K Q J 10 7 4
♡ 2
◇ A J
♣ A 9 3 2

♠ 3
♡ A Q J 10 9 6 5
◇ Q 6 3
♣ 10 4

N-S game
Dealer North

The Bidding

WEST	NORTH	EAST	SOUTH
	1♠	Pass	2♡
Pass	3♠	Pass	4♡
Pass	Pass	Pass	

The Lead

West leads the two of diamonds against your contract of four hearts. How do you plan the play?

Review

Ten tricks appear to be a comfortable target, but if the diamond finesse is right you might make eleven tricks by setting up the spades. How high do you propose to aim?

Solution

One of the first things to ask yourself is how good is your contract. Four hearts is an excellent spot and you can be sure that not everyone will reach it. Some North players will insist on playing in spades and they are almost certain to be defeated. You should therefore concentrate on making four hearts without straining after overtricks.

If you take a losing finesse in diamonds and a club comes back, you may find yourself with a loser in every suit. The sensible line is to go up with the ace of diamonds at trick one and play the king of spades. This will establish a discard for your losing club, and you will lose no more than one spade, one heart and one diamond.

The complete deal:

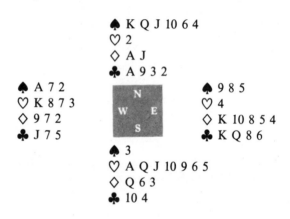

```
                    ♠ K Q J 10 6 4
                    ♡ 2
                    ◇ A J
                    ♣ A 9 3 2
  ♠ A 7 2                              ♠ 9 8 5
  ♡ K 8 7 3          N                 ♡ 4
  ◇ 9 7 2        W       E             ◇ K 10 8 5 4
  ♣ J 7 5            S                 ♣ K Q 8 6
                    ♠ 3
                    ♡ A Q J 10 9 6 5
                    ◇ Q 6 3
                    ♣ 10 4
```

The hand comes from the 1982 World Pairs Championship at Biarritz. In the event, making four hearts was worth 258 of the 334 available match-points, while going one down scored only 124.

[28]

PROBLEM 11

♠ A 7 5 3
♡ A 8 7 6 3
◇ K Q 9
♣ 6

Love all
Dealer East

The Bidding

WEST	NORTH	EAST	SOUTH
		Pass	1 ♠*
Pass	2 ♣	Pass	2 NT**
Pass	3 NT	Pass	Pass
Pass			

* *Five-card major*
** *fewer than 15 points*

The Lead

This is up to you. How do you propose to attack this contract of three no trumps?

Review

The normal lead against a no-trump game is the fourth-highest of your longest suit. Is there a reason to do anything different here?

Solution

In a team game there would be a case for leading a low heart, but at pairs the risk of presenting declarer with a tempo and allowing him to make eleven tricks is too great. Partner can have little in the way of high cards, and your spades are lacking in quality after the ace. Given the chance, declarer is likely to score plenty of tricks in the black suits and you may make no more than your two aces.

If you start with a diamond honour, however, you will be sure of at least three tricks for the defence. Even at teams there is a case for the diamond lead, since partner is more likely to have a number of diamonds headed by the jack than to have anything worth while in hearts. At pairs the diamond lead stands out.

The complete deal:

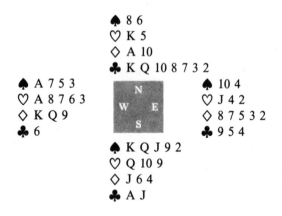

```
                    ♠ 8 6
                    ♡ K 5
                    ◇ A 10
                    ♣ K Q 10 8 7 3 2
   ♠ A 7 5 3                           ♠ 10 4
   ♡ A 8 7 6 3         N               ♡ J 4 2
   ◇ K Q 9         W        E          ◇ 8 7 5 3 2
   ♣ 6                 S               ♣ 9 5 4
                    ♠ K Q J 9 2
                    ♡ Q 10 9
                    ◇ J 6 4
                    ♣ A J
```

This is another hand from the 1982 World Pairs. The diamond lead succeeded in holding declarer to ten tricks, and that was worth 226 out of 334 for the defenders.

PROBLEM 12

♠ 9 6 3
♡ A 7
♦ K Q 4
♣ Q 10 9 4 2

♠ A Q 10 8
♡ Q J 3
♦ A J 7
♣ J 6 5

Love all
Dealer South

The Bidding

SOUTH	WEST	NORTH	EAST
1 ♠	Pass	2 ♣	Pass
2 NT	Pass	3 NT	Pass
Pass	Pass		

The Lead

West leads the five of hearts to the seven, nine and jack.
Hoping to make something of the clubs, you play the five at
trick two. West follows with the three and East captures the
nine with the king. The six of hearts is returned to dummy's ace,
West following with the two. What now?

Review

You might eventually set up enough club tricks for your
contract, but it looks as though the enemy could take five tricks
first. Is there anything else worth trying?

Solution

From the early defence it seems certain that the hearts are divided 5–3, so it doesn't matter who has the ace of clubs. If you play another club at this point you will go one down.

The alternative is to leave the clubs alone and take the double finesse in spades, hoping to find East with both king and jack. You have enough entries in dummy to finesse three times, succeeding even if East has four or five cards in the suit. Is this the only chance?

It is certainly the only chance of making the contract, but at pairs it does not represent the best chance of scoring well. East will have both spade honours only about one time in four, and that weighs the odds too heavily against this line, for you will go two down three-quarters of the time. The sensible course is to give up on the contract and settle for one down by playing another club. All the other declarers will be faced with the same problem, and one down should give you quite a reasonable score.

The complete deal:

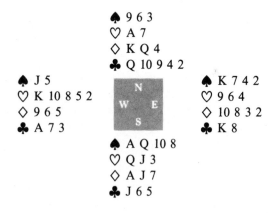

```
                ♠ 9 6 3
                ♡ A 7
                ◇ K Q 4
                ♣ Q 10 9 4 2
  ♠ J 5              N          ♠ K 7 4 2
  ♡ K 10 8 5 2                  ♡ 9 6 4
  ◇ 9 6 5       W       E       ◇ 10 8 3 2
  ♣ A 7 3           S          ♣ K 8
                ♠ A Q 10 8
                ♡ Q J 3
                ◇ A J 7
                ♣ J 6 5
```

PROBLEM 13

```
                    ♠ 10 4
                    ♡ Q 6
                    ◇ A J 10 7 3
                    ♣ A Q 10 5
                                      ♠ Q J 9 2
                         N            ♡ A J 2
Game all            W        E        ◇ 8 5
Dealer South             S            ♣ K 8 7 4
```

The Bidding

SOUTH	WEST	NORTH	EAST
1 NT*	Pass	3 NT	Pass
Pass	Pass		

* *12–14*

The Lead

West leads the five of hearts, the queen is played from dummy and South drops the four under your ace. You continue with the jack of hearts on which South plays the seven and West the three. What now?

Review

Partner appears to have five hearts and he must surely have the king: with ♡ 10 9 8 5 3 he would have led the ten rather than the five. So you can run three more heart tricks to defeat the contract. Is there a reason for doing anything other than play your third heart?

Solution

Since partner is marked with the king of hearts, declarer must have the remaining face-cards with the possible exception of the jack of clubs. That means he has eight top tricks – two spades, five diamonds and the ace of clubs, and if you take your five hearts declarer will take the rest for one down.

Plus 100 is all very well but plus 200 is better, and there is an excellent chance of scoring 200 if you switch to the queen of spades at trick two. The heart pips are such that declarer might think the suit is breaking 6–2. He will view your spade switch as a welcome reprieve, and he will entertain hopes of making his contract (perhaps with overtricks) by taking the club finesse. He is booked for disappointment and a loss of 200.

The complete deal:

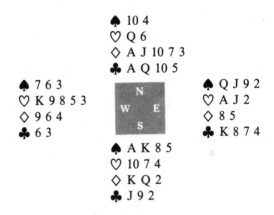

```
                    ♠ 10 4
                    ♡ Q 6
                    ◇ A J 10 7 3
                    ♣ A Q 10 5
    ♠ 7 6 3                          ♠ Q J 9 2
    ♡ K 9 8 5 3          N           ♡ A J 2
    ◇ 9 6 4         W         E      ◇ 8 5
    ♣ 6 3               S           ♣ K 8 7 4
                    ♠ A K 8 5
                    ♡ 10 7 4
                    ◇ K Q 2
                    ♣ J 9 2
```

There is no danger in the spade switch. Declarer may try to embarrass you by running the diamonds, but you can throw two clubs and a spade without discomfort.

Even at teams it would be right to switch to the spade queen at trick three. At pairs such opportunities must not be missed.

PROBLEM 14

♠ 8 5
♡ K Q 4
◇ K J 9 7 4 3
♣ J 4

♠ A K 6
♡ A J 8 7 2
◇ A 5
♣ Q 9 5

Love all
Dealer South

The Bidding

SOUTH	WEST	NORTH	EAST
1 ♡	Pass	2 ◇	Pass
3 NT	Pass	Pass	Pass

The Lead

West leads the four of spades, East puts on the jack and you win with the king. How should you continue?

Review

This is a fine contract. On any normal heart split you have nine tricks on top, and if the diamonds are kind you may make all thirteen tricks. What is the best way of tackling the hand?

Solution

Suppose the diamond finesse is wrong. If you have made it clear that you have five diamond tricks, East is likely to see the need to cash out when he wins the queen. The defenders will take their club winners, holding you to ten tricks in all.

On this sort of hand you must try to lull the defenders into a false sense of security. You might do that by playing the five of diamonds at trick two and finessing the jack. This play gives up a small portion of your chance of making all thirteen tricks (when East has the singleton queen) in exchange for a greatly enhanced chance of making twelve tricks. If East wins with the queen and forms the impression that his partner has the ace, he may think it safe to continue spades. And that could give you twelve tricks for a top score.

The complete deal:

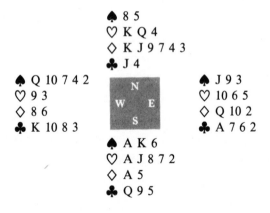

```
                    ♠ 8 5
                    ♡ K Q 4
                    ◇ K J 9 7 4 3
                    ♣ J 4
   ♠ Q 10 7 4 2        N        ♠ J 9 3
   ♡ 9 3          W        E    ♡ 10 6 5
   ◇ 8 6                         ◇ Q 10 2
   ♣ K 10 8 3         S         ♣ A 7 6 2
                    ♠ A K 6
                    ♡ A J 8 7 2
                    ◇ A 5
                    ♣ Q 9 5
```

There are many opportunities for subtle play of this kind in the pairs game.

PROBLEM 15

```
                      ♠ 3
                      ♡ Q J 7
                      ◇ K Q J 9 3
                      ♣ A J 6 5
```

```
                        N
                    W       E
                        S
```

```
                      ♠ A 10 7 2
                      ♡ A K 10 9
N-S game              ◇ 10 6 5
Dealer North          ♣ Q 3
```

The Bidding

WEST	NORTH	EAST	SOUTH
	1 ◇	1 ♠	Dble
Pass	2 ♣	Pass	2 ♡
Pass	3 ♡	Pass	4 ♡
Pass	Pass	Pass	

The Lead

West leads the six of spades and East contributes the jack. How do you plan the play?

Review

In spite of the fact that you have landed in a 4–3 trump fit, the prospects of making at least ten tricks are good. How can you maximise your chances?

Solution

Naturally you start by considering the other possible game contracts. Some pairs are sure to be in three no trumps, and on a spade lead they will score exactly ten tricks, losing two spades and the ace of diamonds. To beat those pairs you will need to score eleven tricks in hearts.

The hearts are not likely to break worse than 4–2, and by far the best way of trying for eleven tricks is by playing low at trick one, allowing East to hold the trick. This retains control of the hand and leaves you with an answer to any move by the defence. You can win a trump switch in hand, ruff a small spade on the table, draw trumps and knock out the ace of diamonds. This will give you one spade, five trumps, four diamonds and a club for what is sure to be an excellent score.

The complete deal:

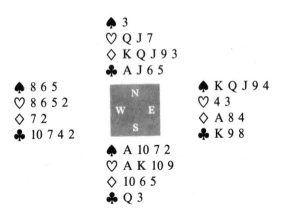

```
                ♠ 3
                ♡ Q J 7
                ◇ K Q J 9 3
                ♣ A J 6 5
  ♠ 8 6 5                          ♠ K Q J 9 4
  ♡ 8 6 5 2          N             ♡ 4 3
  ◇ 7 2          W       E         ◇ A 8 4
  ♣ 10 7 4 2         S             ♣ K 9 8
                ♠ A 10 7 2
                ♡ A K 10 9
                ◇ 10 6 5
                ♣ Q 3
```

Anyone who wins the ace of spades at trick one will have to be satisfied with ten tricks.

PROBLEM 16

♠ J 6
♡ Q 10 7 6 3
♢ J 5 2
♣ A 8 3

♠ Q 10 2
♡ A K 9 5 2
♢ A K 10
♣ K 5

Game all
Dealer South

The Bidding

SOUTH	WEST	NORTH	EAST
1 ♡	Pass	2 ♡	Pass
3 NT	Pass	Pass	Pass

The Lead

West leads the four of spades to his partner's king. East returns the seven of spades to the ace, and West continues with the three of spades. You discard a diamond from dummy, East follows with the five of spades and you win with the queen. How do you plan the play?

Review

Both you and your partner chose mildly eccentric bids on the second round. You might have gone straight to four hearts, while North might have converted to four hearts. At all events it looks as though most of the competitors will play in the heart game. How does that affect your planning?

Solution

You can see that the declarers in four hearts will have an easy path to eleven tricks by setting up a spade trick for a diamond discard in dummy. There will be no need for them to risk the diamond finesse. However, you have no option but to take the diamond finesse if you are to have a chance of eleven tricks, even though this risks being held to nine. The last point need not bother you, for there is unlikely to be much difference between the scores of 600 and 630. To beat the field you need 660.

By all means make sure of your nine tricks first. Run the hearts, cash the ace of diamonds, unblocking the jack from dummy, and play off the king and ace of clubs. Then play the diamond from dummy and finesse the ten. If it is your lucky day you will score a top instead of a bottom.

The complete deal:

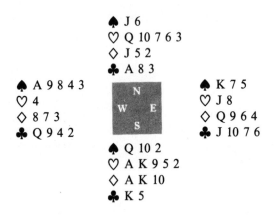

```
                    ♠ J 6
                    ♡ Q 10 7 6 3
                    ◇ J 5 2
                    ♣ A 8 3
 ♠ A 9 8 4 3                          ♠ K 7 5
 ♡ 4               ┌─────────┐        ♡ J 8
 ◇ 8 7 3          │    N    │        ◇ Q 9 6 4
 ♣ Q 9 4 2        │ W     E │        ♣ J 10 7 6
                  │    S    │
                  └─────────┘
                    ♠ Q 10 2
                    ♡ A K 9 5 2
                    ◇ A K 10
                    ♣ K 5
```

PROBLEM 17

```
          ♠ 9 5
          ♡ A Q
          ◇ K Q J 9 5 3
          ♣ 7 6 2
                              ♠ K Q 6 4
                              ♡ 8 5 4
  E-W game                    ◇ A 8 2
  Dealer South                ♣ Q J 4
```

The Bidding

SOUTH	WEST	NORTH	EAST
1 NT*	Pass	3 NT	Pass
Pass	Pass		

12–14

The Lead

West leads the three of clubs to your jack and South's eight. You continue with the queen of clubs on which South plays the ten and West the five. What now?

Review

The defence is off to a good start. Partner clearly has the king of clubs, but he can hardly have an outside entry so there seems little point in continuing clubs. West could have a minor honour in spades, however. A switch to a low spade might conceivably defeat the contract.

Solution

It does not pay to be too greedy in the pairs game. When partner has given you a good start the sensible thing to do is to consolidate, making sure of the tricks that are due to you without taking any risks.

The lead from four clubs headed by the king is by no means automatic. On a heart or a spade lead declarer would probably make ten or eleven tricks. It follows that you can be sure of a good score by holding South to nine tricks, and the way to do that is by switching to the king of spades at trick three. This greatly reduces your chance of defeating the contract, but it is by far the best way of ensuring a good match-point score.

The complete deal:

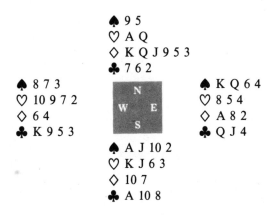

```
                    ♠ 9 5
                    ♡ A Q
                    ◇ K Q J 9 5 3
                    ♣ 7 6 2
  ♠ 8 7 3                           ♠ K Q 6 4
  ♡ 10 9 7 2            N           ♡ 8 5 4
  ◇ 6 4            W       E        ◇ A 8 2
  ♣ K 9 5 3            S            ♣ Q J 4
                    ♠ A J 10 2
                    ♡ K J 6 3
                    ◇ 10 7
                    ♣ A 10 8
```

On the play of a low spade at trick three South has no option but to finesse, and he will score 630 points for an average match-point result.

PROBLEM 18

♠ A 8 5 4
♡ K 10 6 3
◇ 8 6
♣ J 7 5

♠ J 6 2
♡ 9 4
Game all ◇ A K Q 10 5 4
Dealer South ♣ A K

The Bidding

SOUTH	WEST	NORTH	EAST
1 ◇	Pass	1 ♡	Pass
3 ◇	Pass	Pass	Pass

The Lead

West leads the seven of hearts. When you play low from dummy East wins with the jack and returns the three of spades to the jack, king and ace. How do you plan the play?

Review

On an even diamond break you will have no difficulty in making nine tricks, but will this give you a decent match-point score?

Solution

You appear to have fallen below par in the bidding. Both of you were a little conservative. You might have taken a chance on three no trumps on the second round, while partner might have had a shot at three no trumps over your three diamonds. Most of the competitors will be in three no trumps, and it is clear that nine tricks will be laydown if the diamonds break normally. You will gather precious few match-points for making nine tricks in diamonds while others are making nine in no trumps.

In such situations you have to assume that it is your estimate of par, rather than your bidding, that is at fault. If East has four diamonds headed by the jack the declarers in three no trumps, not being gifted with second sight, will go one down. You could equal their scores by playing for the drop in diamonds, but it would be feeble to settle for a tie. Give yourself a chance of turning a bottom into a top by finessing the ten of diamonds on the first round. You have nothing to lose but your zero.

The complete deal:

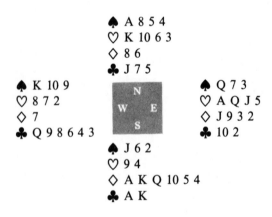

```
                    ♠ A 8 5 4
                    ♡ K 10 6 3
                    ◇ 8 6
                    ♣ J 7 5
  ♠ K 10 9                         ♠ Q 7 3
  ♡ 8 7 2              N           ♡ A Q J 5
  ◇ 7            W          E      ◇ J 9 3 2
  ♣ Q 9 8 6 4 3         S          ♣ 10 2
                    ♠ J 6 2
                    ♡ 9 4
                    ◇ A K Q 10 5 4
                    ♣ A K
```

PROBLEM 19

♠ 7
♡ 8 4
◇ A Q 7 6 3
♣ K Q 9 8 2

♠ 10 9 5 3
♡ 6

E-W game   ◇ J 5 4
Dealer East   ♣ J 7 6 5 4

The Bidding

WEST	NORTH	EAST	SOUTH
		1 ♡	Pass
1 ♠	2 NT	3 ♡	5 ♣
6 ♡	7 ♣	Dble	Pass
Pass	Pass		

The Lead

West leads the ace of hearts and continues with the queen. You ruff and play a club which is won by West with the ace. West plays a spade to his partner's ace and East continues with the queen of spades for dummy to ruff. A trump to your jack clears the suit, West discarding a spade. How do you continue?

Review

You have already lost three tricks and you look like losing another one in diamonds. Will your sacrifice be worth while?

Solution

Losing 700 to save a slam may not be too bad; it depends on how many East-West pairs actually bid the slam. You would be happier if you could hold the loss to 500, for then you would outscore those whose opponents bid no higher than game.

The best chance of avoiding a diamond loser is to find West with king and another, but this in no way equates with the best chance of a good score. If West has the king and another diamond your sacrifice is a phantom, for the slam is defeated by a normal diamond lead. Clearly you must refuse to entertain this possibility.

The only other chance of holding the penalty to 500 is to find someone with a singleton king of diamonds. That is the one to go for. Play a small diamond from hand, and if West plays low go up with the ace, hoping for a singleton king with East.

The complete deal:

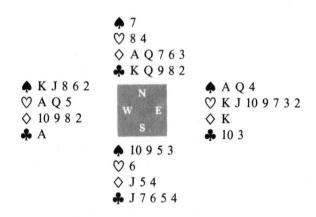

```
                    ♠ 7
                    ♡ 8 4
                    ◇ A Q 7 6 3
                    ♣ K Q 9 8 2
♠ K J 8 6 2              N           ♠ A Q 4
♡ A Q 5          W           E      ♡ K J 10 9 7 3 2
◇ 10 9 8 2              S            ◇ K
♣ A                                 ♣ 10 3
                    ♠ 10 9 5 3
                    ♡ 6
                    ◇ J 5 4
                    ♣ J 7 6 5 4
```

PROBLEM 20

♠ Q 10 9 5 3
♡ K Q
♢ A Q 6 3
♣ 8 4

♠ –
♡ A J 10 4
♢ K 7 5 2
♣ A K Q 6 2

Love all
Dealer South

The Bidding

SOUTH	WEST	NORTH	EAST
1♣	Pass	1♠	Pass
2♢	Pass	2♡	Pass
3♡	Pass	5♢	Pass
6♢	Pass	Pass	Pass

The Lead

West leads the ace of spades, East follows with the four and you ruff with the two of diamonds. How do you continue?

Review

Prospects are good. If you can ruff another spade in hand and then find the trumps 3–2, you should be able to make all thirteen tricks. Is there any cause for concern?

Solution

The danger is that the trumps may break 4–1. In that case if you try to draw trumps, whether you ruff another spade first or not, you will be unable to avoid the loss of two tricks.

There are not many occasions for safety play at pairs but this is surely one of them. You are in a superb slam which few if any of the other pairs will reach. Most will play in three no trumps. Just making your slam will give you an excellent score and you should therefore play as safely as possible.

The best shot is to play a small diamond from both hands at trick two. You can cope with any return. On a trump continuation, for instance, you win in hand, cross to the heart queen, and ruff a second spade with your last trump. Another heart puts dummy in to draw the remaining trumps. Your small clubs go away on the diamonds and your hand is high.

The complete deal:

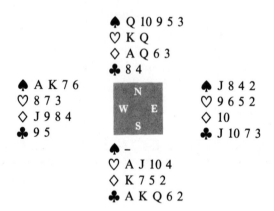

```
              ♠ Q 10 9 5 3
              ♡ K Q
              ◇ A Q 6 3
              ♣ 8 4
  ♠ A K 7 6                    ♠ J 8 4 2
  ♡ 8 7 3         N            ♡ 9 6 5 2
  ◇ J 9 8 4    W     E         ◇ 10
  ♣ 9 5           S            ♣ J 10 7 3
              ♠ –
              ♡ A J 10 4
              ◇ K 7 5 2
              ♣ A K Q 6 2
```

PROBLEM 21

```
              ♠ K J
              ♡ A 8 3
              ◇ K J 10 9 5 4
              ♣ Q 4
                  N         ♠ Q 10 7
                            ♡ K 5
Game all       W   E        ◇ A 8 2
Dealer South       S        ♣ J 9 7 6 3
```

The Bidding

SOUTH	WEST	NORTH	EAST
1 NT*	Pass	3 NT	Pass
Pass	Pass		

12–14

The Lead

West leads the queen of hearts. How do you plan the defence?

Review

Dummy is depressingly strong and it looks as though there will be few tricks for the defence. How do you play to take the maximum?

Solution

Partner appears to have a solid sequence in hearts, in which case declarer must have all the other missing honours. Clearly South can make eleven tricks by winning the second round of hearts and knocking out the ace of diamonds.

Your only advantage is that declarer is ignorant of the heart distribution. You must on no account make the 'normal' play of unblocking the king of hearts when dummy plays low on the first round. There is no point in the unblock since partner cannot have an entry. And if you give declarer reason to believe you have a doubleton, he will realise that he has nothing to lose by winning the heart ace on the second round. You must play low at trick one. Now when partner continues the suit declarer may play low again from dummy, reading you for three hearts. Winning three tricks in defence is likely to give you an excellent score.

The complete deal:

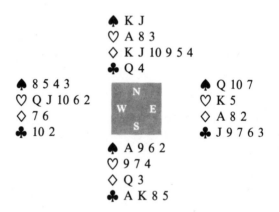

```
                  ♠ K J
                  ♡ A 8 3
                  ◇ K J 10 9 5 4
                  ♣ Q 4
   ♠ 8 5 4 3            N            ♠ Q 10 7
   ♡ Q J 10 6 2                      ♡ K 5
   ◇ 7 6         W          E        ◇ A 8 2
   ♣ 10 2                S           ♣ J 9 7 6 3
                  ♠ A 9 6 2
                  ♡ 9 7 4
                  ◇ Q 3
                  ♣ A K 8 5
```

PROBLEM 22

♠ A 6
♡ 6 5
♢ J 7 5 4
♣ K Q J 9 2

♠ K 2
♡ A K Q 7
♢ K Q 10 3
♣ 10 6 4

Game all
Dealer South

The Bidding

SOUTH	WEST	NORTH	EAST
1 NT	Pass	3 NT	Pass
Pass	Pass		

The Lead

West leads the queen of spades against your no trump game. How do you plan the play?

Review

The opponents have attacked your weak spot and you will not have time to knock out both minor-suit aces. It looks as though you will have to be satisfied with nine tricks – unless you can find a safe way of trying for the overtrick.

Solution

If you win the first spade in hand and play on clubs, someone will take the ace immediately and continue the spade attack. You will then have to run for home with your nine winners.

You might think of trying to slip a diamond past the ace before tackling the clubs, but this is dangerous since if the diamond ace is taken at once you will go down in your contract.

There is a rather better way of trying for an extra trick. Win the first trick with the ace of spades, deliberately squandering dummy's entry. Then play a club to your ten and continue the suit.

The complete deal:

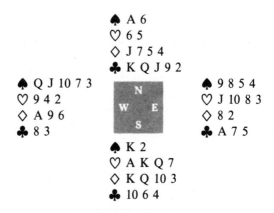

```
                    ♠ A 6
                    ♡ 6 5
                    ◇ J 7 5 4
                    ♣ K Q J 9 2
♠ Q J 10 7 3                    ♠ 9 8 5 4
♡ 9 4 2          N              ♡ J 10 8 3
◇ A 9 6       W     E           ◇ 8 2
♣ 8 3            S              ♣ A 7 5
                    ♠ K 2
                    ♡ A K Q 7
                    ◇ K Q 10 3
                    ♣ 10 6 4
```

Seeing his partner echo in clubs, East may decide to shut out the suit by holding up his ace until the third round. If so, you switch smartly to diamonds and emerge with ten tricks.

East should not go wrong if he asks himself why you did not win the first spade in hand, but players often do not think of such things.

PROBLEM 23

♠ K 8 2
♡ Q 7 5
◇ A K 9 6 5 3
♣ 6

	N	
W		E
	S	

♠ A J 10 7 4
♡ A 8
◇ 8 2
♣ A 7 5 4

Game all
Dealer South

The Bidding

SOUTH	WEST	NORTH	EAST
1 ♠	Pass	2 ◇	Pass
2 ♠	Pass	4 ♠	Pass
Pass	Pass		

The Lead

West leads the three of spades. You play low from the table and capture East's queen with your ace. How should you continue?

Review

There are all sorts of possibilities here. You could ruff a couple of clubs in dummy, you might establish a second trick in hearts, and the diamonds may be capable of development. What is the best match-point line?

Solution

By ruffing clubs you will be safe for ten tricks and have a good chance of an eleventh. But the trump lead has given you an opportunity that will not be available to other declarers and it behoves you to make the most of it. On the simple assumption that the diamonds are 3–2, you can make no fewer than twelve tricks by drawing trumps and ducking a diamond.

Naturally there is no guarantee that the diamonds will divide 3–2, although it is a 68% chance. If the diamonds lie badly you may not even make your contract on this line of play. Nevertheless, at pairs it must be right to seize a chance of making the maximum when it is offered.

The complete deal:

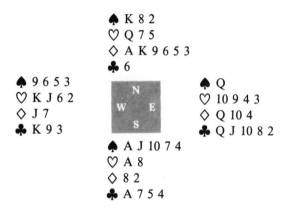

```
                    ♠ K 8 2
                    ♡ Q 7 5
                    ◇ A K 9 6 5 3
                    ♣ 6
   ♠ 9 6 5 3          N          ♠ Q
   ♡ K J 6 2       W     E       ♡ 10 9 4 3
   ◇ J 7              S          ◇ Q 10 4
   ♣ K 9 3                       ♣ Q J 10 8 2
                    ♠ A J 10 7 4
                    ♡ A 8
                    ◇ 8 2
                    ♣ A 7 5 4
```

PROBLEM 24

♠ A
♡ A Q J 10 4 2
♢ Q 4 2
♣ 9 8 4

♠ K 9 2
♡ 6 5
♢ A K J 6 3
♣ A 10 3

N-S game
Dealer West

The Bidding

WEST	NORTH	EAST	SOUTH
Pass	1 ♡	Pass	2 ♢
Pass	3 ♡	Pass	4 ♣
Pass	4 ♢	Pass	6 NT
Pass	Pass	Pass	

The Lead

West leads the four of spades to dummy's ace, East playing the eight. You cross to the king of diamonds, both defenders following, and play a heart for a finesse of the ten. West contributes the three and East the eight. How do you continue?

Review

You can make sure of twelve tricks by continuing with the ace and queen of hearts, but there is a possibility of making all thirteen tricks. Is the play for the overtrick worth the risk involved?

Solution

There are two things that may go wrong if you return to hand with the jack of diamonds and take another heart finesse. East may produce the king, or he may show out on the second round. In either case the defenders are sure to switch to clubs when in with the king of hearts, and your communications will be in a tangle. Unable to enjoy the long hearts *and* the long diamonds, you will have to settle for eleven tricks.

It does not pay to be greedy when you have landed in an excellent slam. Few will play in six hearts, and if you make sure of twelve tricks in no trumps you will outscore those who play in diamonds even if they make an overtrick. All the indications are that you should continue with the ace and queen of hearts to make sure of your slam.

The complete deal:

```
                    ♠ A
                    ♡ A Q J 10 4 2
                    ◇ Q 4 2
                    ♣ 9 8 4
  ♠ J 10 5 4 3          N          ♠ Q 8 7 6
  ♡ K 9 7 3        W       E       ♡ 8
  ◇ 10 5                            ◇ 9 8 7
  ♣ K 6                S           ♣ Q J 7 5 2
                    ♠ K 9 2
                    ♡ 6 5
                    ◇ A K J 6 3
                    ♣ A 10 3
```

PROBLEM 25

```
                    ♠ Q 10 3
                    ♡ 9 6 4
                    ◇ 9 5 3
                    ♣ A 7 6 2
                                      ♠ 9 7 4
                         N            ♡ A J 10 5 3
N-S game            W         E       ◇ 8 2
Dealer West              S            ♣ 9 8 3
```

The Bidding

WEST	NORTH	EAST	SOUTH
Pass	Pass	Pass	2 NT*
Pass	3 NT	Pass	Pass
Pass			

* 20–22

The Lead

West leads the six of diamonds and declarer wins with the jack. South plays the six of spades to the five and queen and returns the four of hearts. How do you defend?

Review

Your choice lies between dashing up with the ace of hearts and playing low to see what develops. Which course is likely to bring in more tricks for the defence?

Solution

It is probably just a matter of saving overtricks, since there is not much chance of defeating this contract. South is bound to have both king and queen of hearts and you cannot prevent him from making them. Partner is marked with some high cards in the minor suits, however. It could be important to use your entry now before his can be knocked out. You should therefore go up with the ace of hearts and return your diamond.

The complete deal:

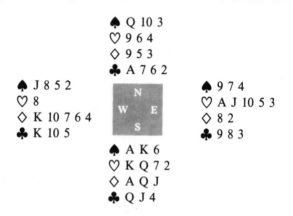

```
              ♠ Q 10 3
              ♡ 9 6 4
              ◇ 9 5 3
              ♣ A 7 6 2
♠ J 8 5 2                      ♠ 9 7 4
♡ 8              N             ♡ A J 10 5 3
◇ K 10 7 6 4   W   E           ◇ 8 2
♣ K 10 5         S             ♣ 9 8 3
              ♠ A K 6
              ♡ K Q 7 2
              ◇ A Q J
              ♣ Q J 4
```

If you play low on the first round of hearts, South will win and play the queen of clubs, ducking in dummy when West covers with the king. He will subsequently score three tricks in each black suit and two in each red, making ten tricks for an above-average score.

When you take the ace of hearts on the first round and return a diamond, declarer is held to nine tricks and it is you who earns the above-average score.

PROBLEM 26

$\spadesuit$ A 4
$\heartsuit$ 10 7 3
$\diamondsuit$ 9 4 3
$\clubsuit$ K 10 9 8 3

$\spadesuit$ K 6 3
$\heartsuit$ A 8 6 2

Game all
Dealer South

$\diamondsuit$ 10 8 5 2
$\clubsuit$ A Q

The Bidding

SOUTH	WEST	NORTH	EAST
1 NT	Pass	Pass	Pass

The Lead

West leads the queen of spades to the four, two and king. How do you plan the play?

Review

Clearly you need to make something of the clubs. You could rely on bringing down the jack in three rounds, or you could make sure of seven tricks by overtaking the queen with the king on the second round and continuing with the ten. Which is the match-point line?

The trouble with the sure-trick line is that plus 90 may not prove to be an adequate match-point score. You have to consider alternative contracts – not so much for your side as for the enemy.

Once again your weak no trump has kept the opponents out of the auction, but they have eight spades between them and it seems likely that two spades will be the contract at some of the other tables. In defence against this contract you have three tricks in the majors plus two or three clubs, depending on whether the suit breaks 3–3 or 4–2. When the clubs are 4–2 two spades will be made, and you can well afford to go one down in one no trump when other pairs are conceding 110.

It is when the clubs are 3–3 and two spades goes down that you must make sure of scoring 120 yourself. Match-point logic therefore indicates that you should not overtake the queen of clubs on the second round. Just unblock the ace and queen and switch to a diamond.

The complete deal:

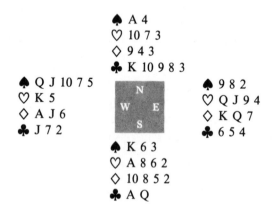

```
                    ♠ A 4
                    ♡ 10 7 3
                    ◇ 9 4 3
                    ♣ K 10 9 8 3
  ♠ Q J 10 7 5                       ♠ 9 8 2
  ♡ K 5            N                  ♡ Q J 9 4
  ◇ A J 6      W       E              ◇ K Q 7
  ♣ J 7 2            S                ♣ 6 5 4
                    ♠ K 6 3
                    ♡ A 8 6 2
                    ◇ 10 8 5 2
                    ♣ A Q
```

PROBLEM 27

♠ A 7 6 3
♡ 6 5 4
♢ A 5 2
♣ A Q 10

♠ K 10 8 2
♡ K J 9 3
♢ 10 9 7
♣ 8 3

Game all
Dealer North

The Bidding

WEST	NORTH	EAST	SOUTH
	1 ♠	Pass	1 NT
Pass	Pass	Pass	

The Lead

West leads the king of diamonds. Declarer wins immediately with the ace and plays a heart from the table. You play the three, South puts in the ten and West contributes the eight. Next comes the five of clubs, and when West plays the two dummy's ten wins the trick. Another heart is played from the table. How do you defend?

Review

That was a rather strange opening bid of one spade on a balanced 14-count. You can't be sure that it has put you at a disadvantage, but the heart position would be clearer if the hand had been played the other way round. You have a choice of three cards to play on this trick. Is one of them any better, or any worse, than the others?

Solution

Declarer must have both the ace and the queen of hearts, and your ambition must be limited to holding him to 120. Partner's eight of hearts may be the start of an echo but it may equally well be a singleton. Declarer could have a 2–5–3–3 shape, and if you are careless he may make nine tricks.

The one card you must not play is the nine of hearts. Declarer knows you to have the jack since his first finesse of the ten succeeded. If you play the nine, he will realise that he cannot hope to make five heart tricks and he will play low, preserving communications. You will be able to cash three diamonds, but South will make the rest for a total of nine tricks and 150.

You should play the jack of hearts, the card you are known to hold, on the second round. Declarer will cover with the queen since he cannot afford to give up the chance of ten tricks when the hearts are 3–2. In practice this will hold him to eight tricks, and he will lose to those who make nine tricks in hearts.

The complete deal:

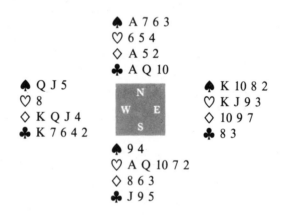

```
              ♠ A 7 6 3
              ♡ 6 5 4
              ◇ A 5 2
              ♣ A Q 10
♠ Q J 5                        ♠ K 10 8 2
♡ 8          N                 ♡ K J 9 3
◇ K Q J 4   W   E              ◇ 10 9 7
♣ K 7 6 4 2     S              ♣ 8 3
              ♠ 9 4
              ♡ A Q 10 7 2
              ◇ 8 6 3
              ♣ J 9 5
```

The play of the king of hearts on the second round will probably succeed as well, but the jack is the natural card.

PROBLEM 28

♠ K 10 6 4
♡ J 6 5
◊ Q 10 7 2
♣ 9 5

♠ A 9 8 5 2
♡ 3
◊ K J 9 4
♣ K 10 7

Game all
Dealer South

The Bidding

SOUTH	WEST	NORTH	EAST
1 ♠	Dble	3 ♠	Pass
Pass	Dble	Pass	Pass
Pass			

The Lead

West leads the ace of hearts and continues with the king. You ruff, play a spade to the jack, king and three, and return the four of spades on which East plays the seven. Do you finesse or play for the drop?

Review

On the bidding the ace of clubs is sure to be with West, so if you guess wrong you will go one down. If you guess correctly you will make your doubled contract. You have to determine in which circumstances you can afford to guess wrong.

Solution

Probabilities are not a great deal of help here. The principle of free choice tells you that the finesse is twice as likely to succeed as the play for the drop, but match-point logic pulls in the opposite direction. A successful finesse will bring in 730 points, but you have no need of these points when the spades are 3–1. Then you will have only three tricks (one spade, one diamond and one club) in defence against the likely enemy contract of four hearts. You can afford to guess wrong when the opponents are cold for game in hearts, for minus 200 will be an excellent score.

It is when the spades are 2–2 and four hearts goes down that you must at all costs make your doubled contract. You should therefore go up with the ace on the second round of spades.

The complete deal:

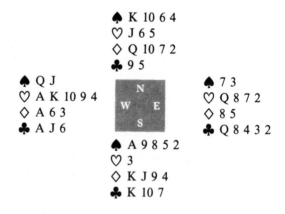

♠ K 10 6 4
♥ J 6 5
♦ Q 10 7 2
♣ 9 5

♠ Q J
♥ A K 10 9 4
♦ A 6 3
♣ A J 6

♠ 7 3
♥ Q 8 7 2
♦ 8 5
♣ Q 8 4 3 2

♠ A 9 8 5 2
♥ 3
♦ K J 9 4
♣ K 10 7

PROBLEM 29

♠ K 10 3
♡ A Q J
♦ A Q 9 4
♣ Q 10 4

♠ Q 6 2
♡ K 7 4
♦ K 7 6 3
♣ K 9 5

```
        N
    W       E
        S
```

N-S game
Dealer North

The Bidding

WEST	NORTH	EAST	SOUTH
	1 ♦	Pass	1 NT
Pass	2 NT	Pass	3 NT
Pass	Pass	Pass	

The Lead

There is little to guide you, but your choice of the two of spades turns out well when partner covers dummy's ten with the jack and declarer plays the five. East returns the four of spades to the seven, queen and king. Next comes the queen of clubs from dummy, East playing the seven and South the two. How do you defend?

Review

With the red kings sitting under the tenaces in dummy, there can be little chance of defeating this contract. What is your defensive trick target?

Solution

This is just a matter of sound defensive technique. Declarer is marked with the black aces, and he probably has the club jack as well. He will need three entries to hand if he is to finesse twice against the king of hearts and once against the king of diamonds. You can deny him one of those entries by refusing to part with the king of clubs on the first round. Hold up the king and make him repeat the finesse.

The complete deal:

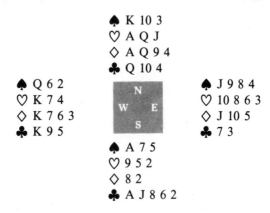

```
                  ♠ K 10 3
                  ♡ A Q J
                  ◇ A Q 9 4
                  ♣ Q 10 4
    ♠ Q 6 2          N          ♠ J 9 8 4
    ♡ K 7 4                      ♡ 10 8 6 3
    ◇ K 7 6 3     W    E         ◇ J 10 5
    ♣ K 9 5          S           ♣ 7 3
                  ♠ A 7 5
                  ♡ 9 5 2
                  ◇ 8 2
                  ♣ A J 8 6 2
```

If you take the club king immediately and return your spade, declarer will win and take a heart finesse. He will then play the ten of clubs, and when East follows it will be safe for him to overtake with the jack. Another heart finesse will be followed by three more clubs and a diamond finesse, giving declarer eleven tricks and an excellent score.

By denying declarer an extra entry you will hold him to ten tricks, which should give you an adequate share of the match points.

PROBLEM 30

♠ A K J 8 6 3
♡ J 4
♦ 10 2
♣ Q J 7

♠ Q 10 5
♡ A Q 10 7
♦ A K 9
♣ 10 9 3

Game all
Dealer South

The Bidding

SOUTH	WEST	NORTH	EAST
1 NT	Pass	2 ♡	Pass
2 ♠	Pass	4 ♠	Pass
Pass	Pass		

The Lead

You reach four spades after a transfer sequence and West leads the king of clubs on which East plays the eight. West continues with the four of clubs to his partner's ace and ruffs the club return. He exits with a trump. How do you plan the play?

Review

You note that anyone in three no trumps is bound to make at least ten tricks. No chance of beating them. In your contract of four spades you have already lost three tricks and need to take the rest. Are you going to take the heart finesse?

Solution

West's gambling opening lead has paid off, putting you at a disadvantage compared with the other declarers in four spades. Some will play from the other side of the table, and even if they play from your hand it is unlikely that any other West player will choose that desperate lead from king small.

Those who do not receive a club lead will draw trumps and take the heart finesse, making eleven tricks if it is right. So a successful heart finesse that brings in ten tricks will be of no use. To have a chance of drawing level with the field you must assume the heart finesse to be wrong and take the double diamond finesse instead.

After two rounds of trumps play the ten of diamonds from dummy, running it if East plays low. If East covers, win with the king, return to dummy with a trump and finesse the nine of diamonds. If it is your lucky day you will be able to discard dummy's losing heart and make as many tricks as any other declarer in four spades.

The complete deal:

```
                    ♠ A K J 8 6 3
                    ♡ J 4
                    ◇ 10 2
                    ♣ Q J 7
  ♠ 9 7 2                              ♠ 4
  ♡ K 9 5 2          N                 ♡ 8 6 3
  ◇ 8 6 5 4       W     E              ◇ Q J 7 3
  ♣ K 4              S                 ♣ A 8 6 5 2
                    ♠ Q 10 5
                    ♡ A Q 10 7
                    ◇ A K 9
                    ♣ 10 9 3
```

PROBLEM 31

♠ Q 5
♡ Q 7 2
◇ Q 10 7 6 3
♣ 8 6 4

♠ K J
♡ A J 6 3
◇ A J 2
♣ A Q 9 5

E-W game
Dealer West

The Bidding

WEST	NORTH	EAST	SOUTH
2 NT	Pass	3 ♡	3 ♠
4 ♡	4 ♠	Dble	Pass
Pass	Pass		

The Lead

You start with the ace of hearts and continue with the three. South ruffs the second heart and plays a low spade which you win with the king, partner following with the four. For want of anything better you continue with a third heart. South ruffs again and plays a spade to the queen, East echoing with the three. Next comes the three of diamonds to the eight, king and ace. How do you continue?

Review

When you have the best hand at the table you want to make the opponents pay a high price for the privilege of playing the hand. How can you best achieve this aim?

Solution

The indications are that declarer's shape is 6–1–3–3. If partner has any honour in clubs, even the ten, you would have made your contract of four hearts in comfort. You would probably have made eleven tricks, in fact, for you would not guess wrong in trumps after the revealing bidding. So you need to defeat the enemy game by four tricks, scoring 700, to compensate adequately for the loss of your game.

You will not score 700 by continuing with the heart force, nor by switching to clubs if declarer has the king. South will draw the last trump and finesse in diamonds to escape for one off.

The way to extract the maximum penalty is to return the jack of diamonds, locking declarer in dummy and forcing him to play clubs himself. You can win the first club, give partner a diamond ruff, and win two further clubs to achieve your target of 700.

The complete deal:

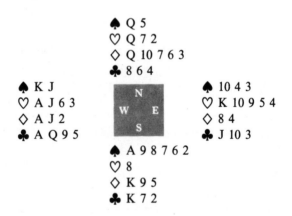

```
                    ♠ Q 5
                    ♡ Q 7 2
                    ◇ Q 10 7 6 3
                    ♣ 8 6 4
  ♠ K J                             ♠ 10 4 3
  ♡ A J 6 3          N              ♡ K 10 9 5 4
  ◇ A J 2        W       E          ◇ 8 4
  ♣ A Q 9 5          S              ♣ J 10 3
                    ♠ A 9 8 7 6 2
                    ♡ 8
                    ◇ K 9 5
                    ♣ K 7 2
```

PROBLEM 32

                    ♠ A 5
                    ♡ 10 3
                    ◇ A K 10 8 7 6 3
                    ♣ A 2

                    ♠ J 9 6 3
                    ♡ A 8 7
Game all   ◇ J 2
Dealer North   ♣ K Q 9 4

The Bidding

WEST	NORTH	EAST	SOUTH
	1 ◇	Pass	1 ♠
Pass	3 ◇	Pass	3 NT
Pass	Pass	Pass	

The Lead

West leads the jack of clubs. How do you plan the play?

Review

The difficulty here is in deciding on your trick target. There is a safety-play to guarantee eleven tricks, but twelve tricks may be there for the taking.

Solution

You can make sure of eleven tricks by winning the ace of clubs and playing a low diamond towards the jack, but you will look foolish (and so will your score) if the suit breaks 2–2 or if someone has the singleton queen. However, it would be rash to win the first trick in dummy and cash a top diamond. You would then be held to eight tricks on a 4–0 break.

At pairs the safety principle has to take a back seat but it need not be completely disregarded. Here you can make a small concession to safety by winning the first trick in hand and playing the two (not the jack) of diamonds. You intend to go up with the ace if West follows suit. When East also follows, you can unblock the ace of clubs and play more diamonds from the top, making eleven or twelve tricks.

If East shows out under the ace of diamonds, you have to continue with a low diamond to the jack. West may hold you to ten tricks by winning and switching to a heart: that is the price you have to pay.

If West shows out on the first diamond, you can make sure of eleven tricks by inserting dummy's ten.

The complete deal:

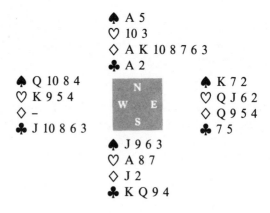

```
              ♠ A 5
              ♡ 10 3
              ◇ A K 10 8 7 6 3
              ♣ A 2
 ♠ Q 10 8 4              ♠ K 7 2
 ♡ K 9 5 4       N       ♡ Q J 6 2
 ◇ –          W     E    ◇ Q 9 5 4
 ♣ J 10 8 6 3    S       ♣ 7 5
              ♠ J 9 6 3
              ♡ A 8 7
              ◇ J 2
              ♣ K Q 9 4
```

PROBLEM 33

♠ A 9 4 3
♡ 5
♢ K Q 10 9
♣ K J 7 4

♠ 7 5
♡ J 7 6 4 2
♢ J 4
♣ A 8 6 3

Game all
Dealer East

The Bidding

WEST	NORTH	EAST	SOUTH
		1 ♡	Pass
2 ♡	Dble	Pass	2 ♠
3 ♡	Pass	Pass	3 ♠
Pass	Pass	Dble	Pass
Pass	Pass		

The Lead

You lead the four of hearts on which partner plays the ace and declarer the queen. East switches to the nine of clubs on which South plays the two. How do you defend?

Review

Tight match-point doubles always make for a tense game. Here you have to decide whether partner started with a singleton or a doubleton club. The pressure comes from the knowledge that a wrong decision may well allow declarer to make his doubled contract.

Solution

Since partner has nothing but the ace in hearts, he will surely have the ace of diamonds along with something good in spades. If he has the king of spades you can count four tricks for the defence. A club ruff is needed to bring the total up to five and achieve the magic score of plus 200.

Partner could have either a singleton or a doubleton club, but there is a sound match-point reason for playing him for a doubleton. If he has a singleton, you will have only three losers in a heart contract. You will have done the wrong thing in the bidding, and a score of 200 will be of little use when others are notching up 620. In such circumstances you must always keep faith with your bidding. Assume that you did the right thing in refusing to go beyond the three-level, which means playing partner for a doubleton club. Play the eight of clubs at trick two.

The complete deal:

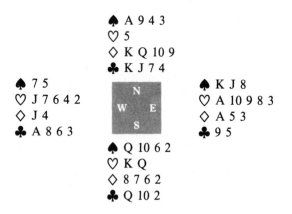

```
                    ♠ A 9 4 3
                    ♡ 5
                    ◇ K Q 10 9
                    ♣ K J 7 4
   ♠ 7 5                              ♠ K J 8
   ♡ J 7 6 4 2          N            ♡ A 10 9 8 3
   ◇ J 4            W       E        ◇ A 5 3
   ♣ A 8 6 3            S            ♣ 9 5
                    ♠ Q 10 6 2
                    ♡ K Q
                    ◇ 8 7 6 2
                    ♣ Q 10 2
```

Partner will win the second spade, play a club to your ace and receive a club ruff to put the contract one down.

PROBLEM 34

♠ 9 7 6 3
♡ A Q J 4
♢ 6
♣ 9 8 6 3

♠ 10 5 4
♡ 2
Love all   ♢ A K 4
Dealer West   ♣ Q J 10 7 5 2

The Bidding

WEST	NORTH	EAST	SOUTH
1 NT*	Pass	Pass	3 ♣
Pass	Pass	3 ♢	Pass
Pass	4 ♣	Dble	Pass
Pass	Pass		

12–14

The Lead

West leads the queen of diamonds to your ace. How do you plan the play?

Review

This is a hazardous enterprise. You are lucky to have avoided the spade lead which would have registered an automatic 300 for your opponents. Now you have the chance of disposing of one of your spade losers, either by a direct finesse in hearts or by a ruffing finesse against East. Which method do you choose?

Solution

As always, you must consider what might have happened in the enemy contract. If West has the king of hearts, three diamonds will be defeated on the automatic heart lead. Partner will win two rounds of hearts and give you a ruff to break the contract. In such circumstances it will do you no good to escape for minus 100, for other pairs will register a plus score your way.

You must go for the option that gives you a chance of a decent score. If East has the king of hearts three diamonds will make. You may ruff away the king of hearts on the second round, but East will discard his remaining heart loser(s) either on clubs or on spades to make his contract. It will be no tragedy for you to lose 100 when other pairs are conceding 110.

You should therefore play a heart to the ace and run the queen on the way back, discarding one of your losing spades.

The complete deal:

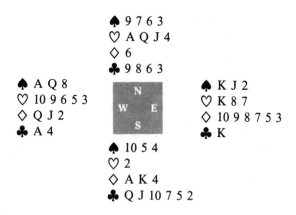

```
                      ♠ 9 7 6 3
                      ♡ A Q J 4
                      ◇ 6
                      ♣ 9 8 6 3
   ♠ A Q 8                              ♠ K J 2
   ♡ 10 9 6 5 3         N              ♡ K 8 7
   ◇ Q J 2          W       E          ◇ 10 9 8 7 5 3
   ♣ A 4                S              ♣ K
                      ♠ 10 5 4
                      ♡ 2
                      ◇ A K 4
                      ♣ Q J 10 7 5 2
```

PROBLEM 35

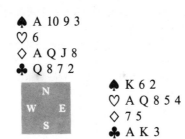

♠ A 10 9 3
♡ 6
♢ A Q J 8
♣ Q 8 7 2

♠ K 6 2
♡ A Q 8 5 4
♢ 7 5
♣ A K 3

Game all
Dealer East

The Bidding

WEST	NORTH	EAST	SOUTH
		1 ♡	Pass
2 ♡	Dble	3 ♡	3 ♠
Pass	Pass	Dble	Pass
Pass	Pass		

The Lead

West leads the two of hearts to your ace, and you test the water with the king of clubs, South playing the six and West the five. When you switch back to a low heart West covers the nine with his ten and dummy ruffs. A club is played from the table and you go up with the ace. South drops the jack and West the four. Another small heart brings forth the jack from South and the king from West. Declarer ruffs in dummy and plays the ace of spades followed by the ten to your king, partner playing the four and the seven. What now?

Review

You have your book of four tricks and need just one more to justify the double. Where might that trick come from?

Solution

Declarer is marked with a 4–3–4–2 shape, and if his top diamond is as good as the ten you are not going to defeat the contract. On a heart continuation South will ruff, draw the last trump, and finesse in diamonds for nine tricks. Come to think of it, on a heart return South does not need the ten of diamonds, for West will be squeezed in the minor suits and forced to yield the contract.

The only play to give you a chance is to return your club. South will not be able to ruff this without destroying the club menace, and if he wins in dummy and ruffs a club, dummy will be one-suit-squeezed on the play of the last trump.

The complete deal:

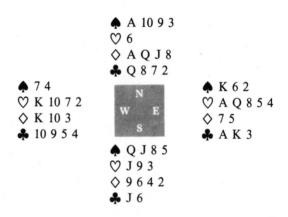

```
                  ♠ A 10 9 3
                  ♡ 6
                  ◇ A Q J 8
                  ♣ Q 8 7 2
  ♠ 7 4                          ♠ K 6 2
  ♡ K 10 7 2         N           ♡ A Q 8 5 4
  ◇ K 10 3        W     E        ◇ 7 5
  ♣ 10 9 5 4         S           ♣ A K 3
                  ♠ Q J 8 5
                  ♡ J 9 3
                  ◇ 9 6 4 2
                  ♣ J 6
```

Do you see declarer's mistake? If he had cashed the queen of clubs before playing the second spade you would have no way of preventing him from scoring 730.

Partner's mistake? Well, an initial trump lead holds declarer to eight tricks.

PROBLEM 36

♠ J 4
♡ K J 10 3
◇ A K J 7
♣ J 9 4

♠ 8 5
♡ A 9 8 6 2
◇ Q 9 6 5
♣ 10 3

E-W game
Dealer West

The Bidding

WEST	NORTH	EAST	SOUTH
1 ♠	Dble	3 ♠	4 ♡
Dble	Pass	Pass	Pass

The Lead

West cashes the ace and king of clubs and switches to the ace and another spade. East wins the second spade with the king and plays the queen of clubs. You ruff with the eight of hearts and heave a sigh of relief when West follows with the six of clubs. The ace of hearts produces the four from West and the seven from East, and West plays the five on the next round. Do you finesse or play for the drop?

Review

There is no real clue from the bidding. West does not need the queen of hearts to double your game. A wrong guess at this point will result in minus 300 instead of minus 100.

Solution

The theme is similar to that of Problem 28. In order to come up with the right match-point decision you have to consider how the opponents would have fared in their contract. In defence against spades you have a maximum of two tricks in each red suit. And you will make four tricks only if the hearts are 2–2. So if East has a singleton heart you do not need the finesse, even though it will save a trick. Minus 300 will be good enough when the opponents are cold for four spades.

It is when the hearts are 2–2 and four spades goes down that you must make sure of escaping for one down. Minus 100 will be a good save against *three* spades.

You should therefore play for the drop, secure in the knowledge that you will score well whether East shows out or not.

The complete deal:

```
                    ♠ J 4
                    ♡ K J 10 3
                    ◇ A K J 7
                    ♣ J 9 4
   ♠ A Q 10 7 2          N          ♠ K 9 6 3
   ♡ 5 4            W         E      ♡ Q 7
   ◇ 10 4 2                          ◇ 8 3
   ♣ A K 6              S           ♣ Q 8 7 5 2
                    ♠ 8 5
                    ♡ A 9 8 6 2
                    ◇ Q 9 6 5
                    ♣ 10 3
```